atedge

Microview 9

Publisher / Editor	Glen R. Serbin
Vice President	Elizabeth Nebb Owen
Project Design	Howry Design Associates, San Francisco
Marketing	Beverly Adler, Susan Baraz
Advisory Board	William Claxton, Photographer
	Andrea Kaye, Vice President, McCann-Erickson, Inc.
	Beverly Don, Art Buyer, Merkley + Partners
	G. Ray Hawkins, G. Ray Hawkins Gallery
	Alec Vianu, Creative Director, Concept Soup
	Max Fallon
International Director of Production	Tamra Dempsey
Production Manager	Barbara Kuhn
Production Staff	Theil Shelton, Kiyoshi Takami
Editorial Proofing	Julie Simpson
Controller	Radana Khadilkar
Distribution Coordinator	Kimberly Harvey
Administrative Support	Kim Taylor
Printer	Toppan Printing Co., Ltd., Tokyo

LA / NY

AtEdge™ Microview 9 is published by
Serbin Communications, Inc.
800 876 6425
e-mail: admin@at-edge.com
www.at-edge.com

813 Reddick Street
Santa Barbara, California 93103

45 Rockefeller Plaza, Suite 2000
New York, New York 10111

atedge

A continuing series of publications that connects top-echelon assignment photographers with the world's most active and influential art directors. By invitation only, AtEdge is a fast and flexible program designed to allow this elite group of photographers to show fresh, new work all year long. AtEdge presents commercial photography in a premium fine art environment, challenging creative buyers to break away from tradition.

AtEdge. Where visionaries unite.

Photographers

Eric Schmidt

represented by

Elizabeth Pojé
elizabethpoje.com

Los Angeles
310 556 1439

New York
212 222 2921

Midwest Associate
414 962 3109

ericschmidtphotography.com

Ron Berg

represented by

Elizabeth Pojé
elizabethpoje.com

Los Angeles
310 556 1439

New York
212 222 2921

Midwest Associate
414 962 3109

ronbergphoto.com

Tony Garcia

represented by

Elizabeth Pojé
elizabethpoje.com

Los Angeles
310 556 1439

New York
212 222 2921

Midwest Associate
414 962 3109

tonygarcia.com

John Christenson

represented by

Amanda Grace
323 309 6112

Studio
johnchristenson.com
612 343 7474

Vic Huber

represented by

Stephen Bishop
vichuber.com
949 261 5844

Ron Derhacopian

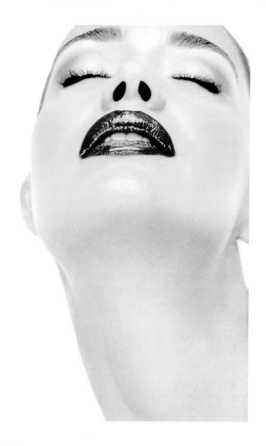

represented by

Kimberly Klein   *Los Angeles*   *New York*
vistalux.com   *323 933 7800*   *646 644 6965*

ronderhacopian.com

George Fulton

represented by

Kimberly Klein
vistalux.com

Los Angeles
323 933 7800

New York
646 644 6965

georgefulton.com

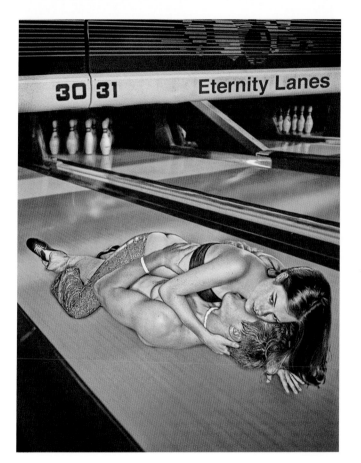

Walter Iooss

represented by

Stockland Martel
stocklandmartel.com
212 727 1400

Richard Corman

represented by

Stockland Martel
stocklandmartel.com
212 727 1400

Jim Fiscus

represented by

Stockland Martel
stocklandmartel.com
212 727 1400

Studio
fiscusphoto.com
404 577 8744

Ruedi Hofmann

represented by

Stockland Martel
stocklandmartel.com
212 727 1400

Nadav Kander

represented by

Stockland Martel
stocklandmartel.com
212 727 1400

Bill Charles London
billcharles.com
+44 207 033 9284

PH Print
PH-print.com
+33 1 4412 3000

www.nadavkander.com

Jeff Mermelstein

represented by

Bill Charles Inc.
billcharles.com
212 965 1465

Larry Fink

represented by

Bill Charles Inc.
billcharles.com
212 965 1465

Mark Laita

represented by

Los Angeles studio
marklaita.com
310 836 1645

Robin Dictenberg
New York
212 620 0995

Jodie Zeitler
Chicago
312 467 9220

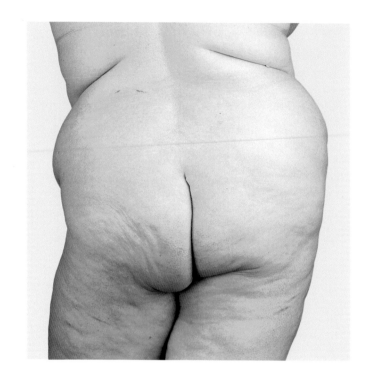

Sandro

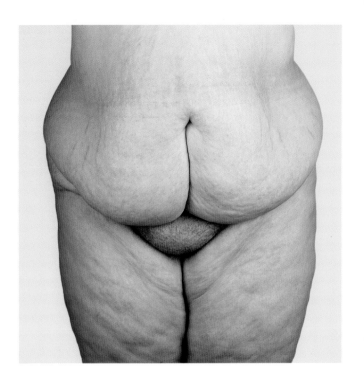

represented by

Robin Dictenberg
East/West
212 620 0995

Randi Fiat
Midwest
847 835 3999

Studio
sandrofilm.com
773 486 0300

Simon Stock

page

52

represented by

Robin Dictenberg
simonstock.com
212 620 0995

Gozo

represented by

Greenhouse   gozoprod.com
greenhousereps.com
212 661 0111

David Waldorf

represented by

Greenhouse
greenhousereps.com
212 661 0111

davidwaldorf.com

Rosanne Olson

represented by

Cynthia Held   *rosanneolson.com*
heldanda.com
323 655 2979

Vincent Dente

represented by

Cynthia Held
heldanda.com
323 655 2979

dentestudio.com

Jim Krantz

represented by

Cynthia Held   fotoj.com
cynthiaheld.com
323 655 2979

Greg Slater

page

64

represented by

Terry Squire
gregslater.com
919 772 1262

Max Hirshfeld

contact

maxpix.com

Washington
202 363 4660

George Simhoni

represented by

Westside Studio
westsidestudio.com
416 535 1955

Midwest
Somlo Talent
somlotalent.com
312 421 2229

Nancy Newberry

contact

nancynewberry.com
214 563 5603

Richard Hamilton Smith

contact

richardhamiltonsmith.com
218 732 2600

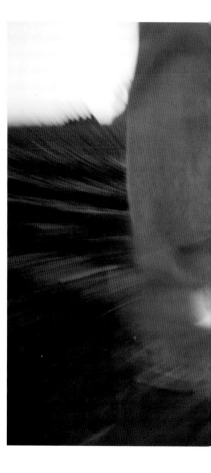

Monika Merva

page

74

contact

monikamerva.com

New York
718 596 8095

Paul Aresu

represented by

Barry Goldring
paularesu.com
212 604 0606

Barbara Vincent
Connecticut
203 322 2332

Quitze Nelson
Dallas
214 660 0887

Keith Finger
Atlanta
770 971 6760

Tom Hassler

78

contact

tomhasslerphoto.com
503 228 8338

John Lawton

represented by

CPR
www.agencycpr.com
212 737 4255

page

represented by

Jock McDonald

82

Friend & Johnson, Inc.
friendandjohnson.com

East
212 337 0055

West
415 927 4500

Midwest
312 435 0055

Vincent Dixon

represented by

Friend & Johnson, Inc.
friendandjohnson.com

East
212 337 0055

West
415 927 4500

Midwest
312 435 0055

vincentdixon.com

Geof Kern

represented by

Friend & Johnson
friendandjohnson.com

geofkern.com
214 630 0856

Claudia Goetzelmann

contact

claudiagoetzelmann.com

San Francisco
415 305 7425

Steve Bronstein

represented by

b-hive
bhivepro.com
212 925 2999

Sally Gall

represented by

b-hive
bhivepro.com
212 925 2999

Dave Nagel

contact

nagelphoto.com

Los Angeles
310 275 7110

Heimo

contact

heimophotography.com

San Francisco
415 298 2653

Jim Scherer

represented by

Katherine Hennessy
kate-company.com
617 549 9872

Jörg Meyer

represented by

*Katherine Hennessy
kate-company.com
617 549 9872*

Paul Elledge

represented by

virtū
www.virtu.ws

Chicago
312 397 9888

New York
212 989 8880

San Francisco
415 898 9888

www.paulelledge.com

Lars Topelmann

represented by

virtū
www.virtu.ws

Chicago
312 397 9888

New York
212 989 8880

San Francisco
415 898 9888

larstopelmann.com

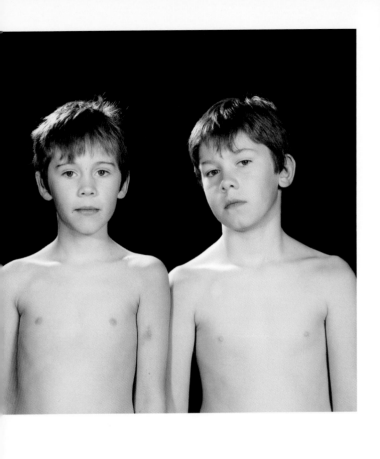

Peter Zander

contact

PeterZander.com

Northeast
914 248 5924

RJ Muna

page

108

represented by

Marianne Campbell Associates
rjmuna.com
415 433 0353

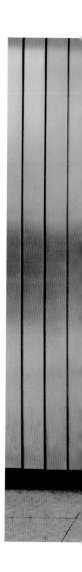

James Salzano

represented by

Marianne Campbell Associates
mariannecampbell.com
415 433 0353

Salzano Studio, Inc.
salzanophoto.com
212 242 4820

Christopher Irion

represented by

Freda Scott, Inc.
fredascott.com
415 550 9121

Tom Maloney
tommaloneyreps.com
312 704 0500

irionphotography.com

Michael McRae

contact

michaelmcrae.com

Salt Lake City
801 328 3633

Scogin Mayo

contact

scoginmayo.com
214 394 4596

Michael Falco

119

represented by

Tricia Weber
thewebergroup.net
212 799 6532

Falcophoto.com

Rainer Stratmann

page

120

represented by

Shelly Steichen
steichenrepresents.com
949 489 1938

Bill Cash

represented by

Shelly Steichen
steichenrepresents.com
949 489 1938

Studio
billcashphoto.com
310 541 5909

Chris Gordaneer

represented by

Randy Cole Represents
randycole.com
212 679 5933

William Moran

page

126

contact

wmphotographs.com

San Francisco
415 255 9631

Patrick Molnar

represented by

Robert Mead Associates
rmeadimage.com
860 245 0276

patmolnar.com

Matthew Mahon

contact

matthewmahon.com

Austin
512 797 8831

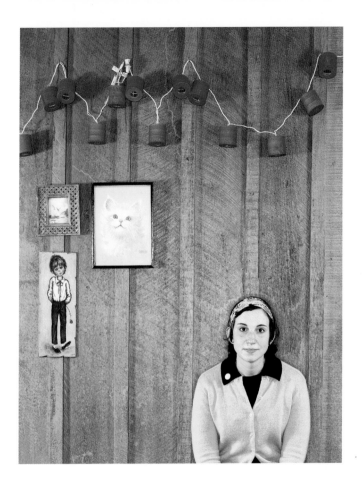

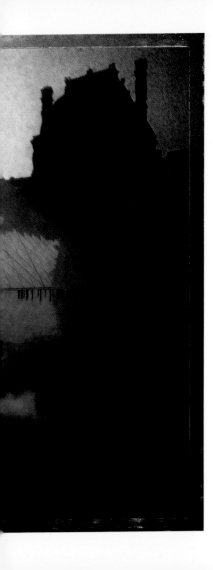

Graham Brown

contact

photograham.com

Minneapolis
612 332 3905

Andrew Martin

represented by

Toni McNaughton
312 855 1225

Studio
andrewmartin.com
312 226 1511

Dan Hallman

page

136

represented by

Proof
proofphoto.com
212 727 7445

danhallman.com

Mark Seliger

represented by

Proof
proofphoto.com
212 727 7445

Jimmy Williams

represented by

Jennifer Tomassi
East
jwproductions.com
919 832 5971

Natalie Ogura
West
jwproductions.com
512 507 2002

Thomas Heinser

represented by

Elyse Connolly
thomasheinser.com
212 255 0886

Howard Schatz

represented by

Beverly Ornstein
howardschatz.com
212 334 6667

Noel Barnhurst

146

represented by

Heather Elder
heatherelder.com
415 285 7709

noelbarnhurst.com

Andy Anderson

represented by

Heather Elder
heatherelder.com
415 285 7709

andyandersonphoto.com

Thomas Broening

represented by

Heather Elder
thomasbroening.com
415 285 7709

Ann Cutting

represented by

Heather Elder
heatherelder.com
415 285 7709

Los Angeles Studio
cutting.com
626 440 1974

David Martinez

represented by

Heather Elder
heatherelder.com
415 285 7709

davidmartinezstudio.com

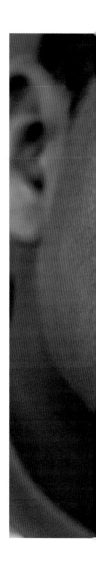

Hunter Freeman

page

156

represented by

Heather Elder
heatherelder.com
415 285 7709

San Francisco Studio
hunterfreeman.com
415 252 1910

Mark Richards

page

158

represented by

Deborah Ayerst
debayerst.com
415 567 3570

Davies + Starr

represented by

Deborah Ayerst
debayerst.com
415 567 3570

Pier Nicola D'Amico

represented by

Deborah Ayerst
debayerst.com
415 567 3570

Moshe Katvan

katvan.com

New York
212 242 4895

Christian Weber

represented by

@radical.media
christianweber.net
212 462 1500

Grégoire Alexandre

represented by

The Daylight Co.
thedaylightco.com
212 334 1120

David Meredith

represented by

The Daylight Co.
thedaylightco.com
212 334 1120

Chad Holder

contact

chadholder.com
612 384 7553

Naomi Harris

page

175

represented by

LaNette Hodge
212 226 5212

Studio
naomiharris.com
917 687 0886

Tatjana Alvegaard

contact

alvegaard.com

Midwest
913 219 4645

Frank Herholdt

represented by

Judith Miller Inc.
USA
judithmillerinc.com
212 564 0216

Agent Orange
Europe
agentorange.co.uk
+44 020 7833 5878

William Huber

represented by

Marilyn Cadenbach Associates
cadenbach.com

Los Angeles
310 399 8442

New York
212 627 8872

Peter Keil

represented by

Marilyn Cadenbach Associates
cadenbach.com

Los Angeles
310 399 8442

New York
212 627 8872

John Huet

represented by

Marilyn Cadenbach   Los Angeles   New York
Associates   310 399 8442   212 627 8872
cadenbach.com

Mark Hooper

contact

markhooper.com

Portland
503 223 3135

Jeff Zaruba

contact

zarubaphotography.com

San Francisco
415 457 3223

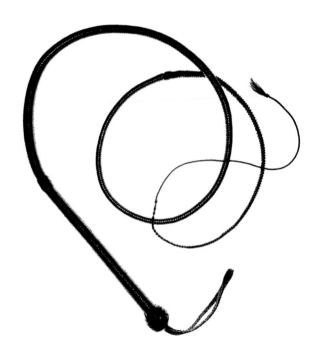

Tom Schierlitz

contact

tomschierlitz.com
212 431 4195

Chris Callis

contact

chriscallis.com

New York
718 638 5150

Charles Klein

contact

charleskleinphotography.com

West
510 525 7947

Rodney Smith

page

196

contact

rodneysmith.com

New York
845 359 3814

Bruce Davidson

represented by

Magnum Photos
magnumphotos.com
212 929 6000 x 110

represented by

Harry De Zitter

Nowicki's Inc.
nowickisinc.com
781 444 3575

Frans Kuypers
franskuypers.com
+31 26 445 1111

Gigi Des Fontaines
shapeshifters-photo.com
+27 21 461 6064

dezitter.com
239 352 0500

Kevin Banna

represented by

Marsha Pinkstaff
pinkstaff.com
212 799 1500

Erica Chadwick
ericachadwick.com
773 856 0614

kevinbanna.com

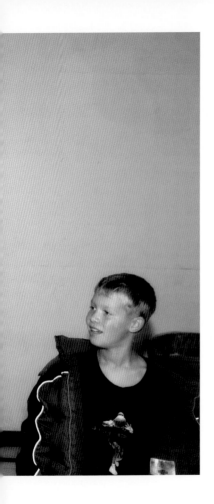

Bill Frakes

represented by

Marsha Pinkstaff
pinkstaff.com
212 799 1500

Peter Rodger

represented by

Norman Maslov
maslov.com
415 641 4376

Marsha Pinkstaff
pinkstaff.com
212 799 1500

Cristiana Ceppas

represented by

Norman Maslov   *ceppas.com*
maslov.com
415 641 4376

David Maisel

Norman Maslov   davidmaisel.com
maslov.com
415 641 4376

Deborah Jones

represented by

Norman Maslov
maslov.com
415 641 4376

Michele Clement

represented by

Norman Maslov
maslov.com
415 641 4376

David Allan Brandt

represented by

Norman Maslov
maslov.com
415 641 4376

davidallanbrandt.com

Michael Lavine

contact

michaellavine.com

New York
212 274 9525

Fred Licht

contact

fredlicht.com
818 790 1400

Lance W Clayton

contact

lancewclayton.com

West
801 631 3475

Brent Humphreys

224

represented by

Marcel Saba
brenthumphreys.com
212 253 0399

Stan Musilek

contact

musilek.com

San Francisco
415 621 5336

Paris
+33 14 338 4464

AR Minkkinen

page

229

contact

arnorafaelminkkinen.org

*Boston
978 771 8200*

Adrian Wilson

represented by

Interior Photography Inc.
interiorphotography.net
212 729 7077

represented by

Korman + Company
kormanandcompany.com
212 402 2450
626 583 1442

cottonmuttonbones
cottonmuttonbones.co.uk
+44 0207 723 3100

michaelprince.com

Marc Ohrem-Leclef

represented by

Ray Brown Productions
raybrownpro.com
212 243 5057

Nerger-Mao
nergermao.com
+49 40 450 0812

marcleclef.com

David Emmite

contact

davidemmite.com

Portland
503 239 5135

Bill Miles

page

238

represented by

Barbara Laurie
barbaralaurie.com
212 725 1411

Alan Cresto

page

240

represented by

Bernstein & Andriulli
ba-reps.com
212 682 1490

Stephen Wilkes

represented by

Bernstein & Andriulli
ba-reps.com
212 682 1490

Steve Hix

represented by

Karen Russo
New York
212 749 6382

Emily Inman
Midwest
312 836 9103

Studio
hixphoto.com
512 693 7100

page

Stewart Cohen   246

represented by

Denise Stewart	*Emily Inman*	*Joe Lombardo*
dsagent.com	*emilyinman.com*	*igroupnyc.com*
214 942 1360	*312 836 9103*	*212 564 3970*

L'enfant Bleu – French Children's Charity bringing
more awareness to the issues of child abuse

Chris Frazer Smith

represented by

Anderson Hopkins
andersonhopkins.com
212 431 5117

Frank Meyl

represented by

Anderson Hopkins
andersonhopkins.com
212 431 5117

Garry Simpson

represented by

Anderson Hopkins
andersonhopkins.com
212 431 5117

Craig Cameron Olsen   254

represented by

Anderson Hopkins
andersonhopkins.com
212 431 5117

Giblin & James

represented by

Anderson Hopkins
andersonhopkins.com
212 431 5117

Kevin Zacher

represented by

Anderson Hopkins
andersonhopkins.com
212 431 5117

Micheal McLaughlin

represented by

Julian Richards
julianrichards.com
212 219 1269

michealmclaughlin.com

Jill Greenberg

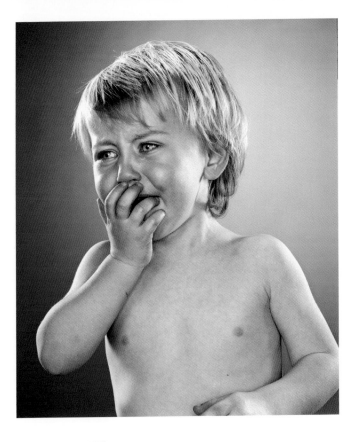

represented by

Art Mix
manipulator.com

East
212 989 4996

West
310 473 0770

Dirk Karsten

represented by

Rhoni Epstein Associates
rhoniepstein.com

West
310 207 593

East
917 597 7211

www.dirkkarsten.com

Jesse Diamond

represented by

Rhoni Epstein Associates
rhoniepstein.com

West
310 207 5937

East
917 597 7211

jessediamond.com

J Bennett Fitts

page

268

represented by

Rhoni Epstein Associates
rhoniepstein.com

West
310 207 5937

East
917 597 7211

jbennettfitts.com

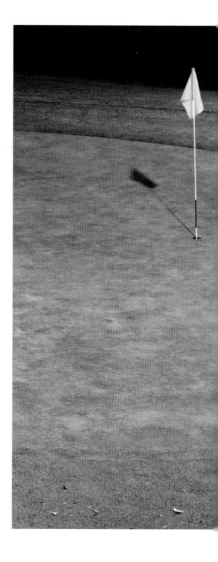

Michele Dugan

represented by

Rhoni Epstein Associates
rhoniepstein.com

West
310 207 5937

East
917 597 7211

duganphoto.com

Ron Eshel

represented by

Rhoni Epstein Associates
rhoniepstein.com

West
310 207 5937

East
917 597 7211

roneshel.com

Erik Almås

represented by

Tidepool
erikalmas.com

415 643 1231

Timothy Archibald

represented by

Tidepool
tidepoolreps.com
415 643 1231
310 925 6783

Studio
510 758 4778

Patrick Barta

contact

Lyn Porterfield   bartaphoto.com
206 343 7644
888 343 7644

Glen Wexler

contact

glenwexler.com

Los Angeles
323 465 0268

Dazeley

represented by

Sarah Ryder Richardson
www.peterdazeley.com
+ 44 20 7736 2999

Neal Brown

represented by

Sharpe + Associates
sharpeonline.com
310 641 8556

Eric Tucker

286

represented by

Sharpe + Associates
sharpeonline.com
310 641 8556

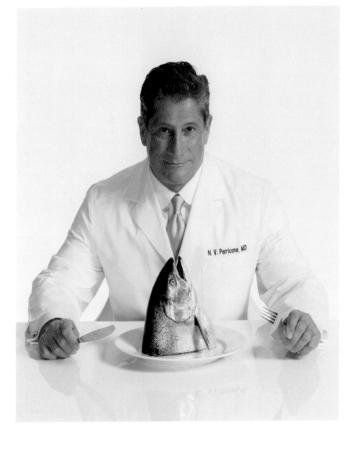

Hugh Kretschmer

represented by

Sharpe + Associates
sharpeonline.com
310 641 8556

Jamey Stillings

represented by

Sharpe + Associates
sharpeonline.com
310 641 8556

jameystillings.com

Peter Leverman

292

contact

peterleverman.com
800 851 4524

Marshall Harrington

contact

harringtonstudio.com

West Coast
619 291 2775

Julia Fullerton-Batten

Bob Stevens

298

represented by

LG
bobstevens.com
310 798 2881

Tyler Gourley

represented by

Arlene Johnson & Associates
arlenejohnsonreps.com
415 543 1131

tylergourley.com

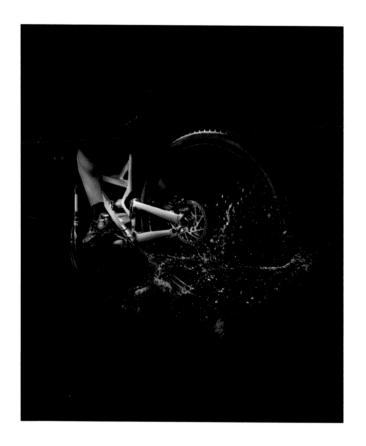

Dan Escobar

represented by

Arlene Johnson & Associates
West
arlenejohnsonreps.com
415 543 1131

John Kenney
East
jkand.com
914 962 0002

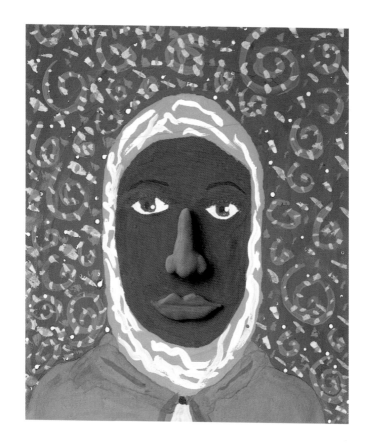

Shawn Michienzi

represented by

John Kenny
East
jkand.com
914 962 0002

Tricia Burlingham
West
artistrepinc.com
818 953 7300

Fredrik Brodén

represented by

Renée Rhyner and Company   fredrikbroden.com
reneerhyner.com
214 922 7072

Sophie Olmsted

represented by

Redux Pictures
reduxpictures.com
212 253 0399

Bret Wills

contact

bretwills.com

New York
212 904 1866

Mark Tucker

contact

MergeLeft Reps, Inc.
mergeleftreps.com
212 840 0321

marktucker.com

Jeff Sedlik

contact

sedlik.com

Los Angeles
213 626 3323

New York
212 447 1255

Evan Kafka

represented by

Snyder & Co.
snyderandcompany.com
212 925 8203

evankafka.com

Arthur Meyerson

contact

arthurmeyerson.com

Houston
713 529 9697